Goodnight Prayers

Illustrations by Maureen Bradley

A LITTLE LION

By day and night

Father, unto you we raise
Hearts and voices full of praise.
Bless us waking, guard us sleeping,
Through this night and all our days.

When I'm frightened

Dear God, sometimes
I get frightened at night.
Please look after me tonight.

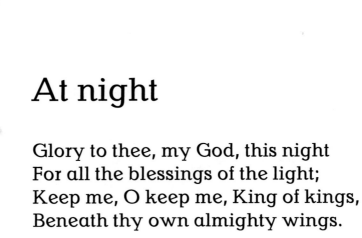

At night

Glory to thee, my God, this night
For all the blessings of the light;
Keep me, O keep me, King of kings,
Beneath thy own almighty wings.

A bedtime prayer

Jesus, tender Shepherd, hear me;
Bless your little lamb tonight;
Through the darkness please be near me;
Keep me safe till morning light.

All this day your hand has led me,
And I thank you for your care;
You have warmed and clothed and fed me;
Listen to my evening prayer.

My friends

Thank you, God, for my friends;
We've had such fun today.
I can hardly wait for tomorrow
when we next go out to play.

For children everywhere

O God, our heavenly Father,
bless and keep your children
all over the world,
this night and for ever.

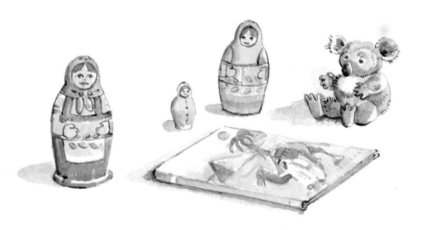

Jesus, friend of little children

Jesus, friend of little children,
Be a friend to me;
Take my hand and ever keep me
Close to thee.

Sorry

Loving Father, I'm sorry for the wrong things
that I have said or thought or done today.
I'm sorry if I made others unhappy,
but most of all, help me to be sorry
if I have hurt you.

In bed

Now that I'm sleepy, God,
I thank you for bedtime stories,
for my warm, cosy bed and
for someone to tuck me in at night.

Never alone

In our work and play God leads us,
Every step we take.
In our sleep he will be near us,
Watching till we wake.

On a moonlit night

The moon shines bright,
The stars give light
Before break of day;
God bless you all
Both great and small
And send a joyful day.

Compilation copyright © 1993 Lion Publishing
Illustrations copyright © 1993 Maureen Bradley

Published by
Lion Publishing plc
Sandy Lane West, Oxford, England
ISBN 0 7459 2842 0 (casebound)
ISBN 0 7459 2640 1 (paperback)
Albatross Books Pty Ltd
PO Box 320, Sutherland, NSW 2232, Australia
ISBN 0 7324 0771 0 (casebound)
ISBN 0 7324 0643 9 (paperback)

First edition 1978
This revised edition 1993

10 9 8 7 6 5 4 3 2 1

Acknowledgments
We thank those who have given us permission to include prayers
in this book and apologize if there are any copyright omissions.
Scripture Union: from *Let's Talk to God* by Zinnia Bryan,
'Loving Father, I'm sorry for all the wrong things'.

A catalogue record for this book is available
from the British Library

Printed and bound in Slovenia

6987